The
Little
Book of
ECOSYSTEM
SERVICES
in the city

Jon Sadler, Nick Grayson, James Hale, Martin Locret-Collet, Daniel Hunt,
Chris Bouch and Chris Rogers

Acknowledgements

This book is an output from the Liveable Cities project, which was funded by the UK Engineering and Physical Sciences Research Council under grant EP/J017698/1. It was a collaborative programme grant undertaken by researchers at the University of Birmingham, Lancaster University, University of Southampton and University College London, led by Professor Chris Rogers.

We are grateful for the contributions of all our colleagues on this project and to the participants who attended the workshop in Birmingham, interviewees who freely made available their time and the Council Officers in our case study cities who supported the work. Special thanks to Drs. Serena Pollastri and Christopher T. Boyko for developing and designing the Highbury Parks (Green) Summit.

Contents

4

What this little book tells you

This little book tells you about the findings of research into the provision of ecosystem services in cities undertaken as part of the Liveable Cities project. It is based on a systematic review of the academic literature, conversations with researchers, interviews with people engaged with greenspaces in cities (as part of a linked PhD programme by one of us – Martin Locret-Collet), a comparative examination of green infrastructure and ecosystem services in three case studies cities (Birmingham, Lancaster and Southampton), a workshop about the future of parks with citizens of Birmingham in 2016 and on-going strategic policy initiatives in the City of Birmingham aimed at making Natural Capital (NC) a pivotal part of a framework for integrating ecological services into policy delivery.

Our research has shown that 'business as usual' is failing to protect Urban Green Infrastructure (UGI), which is important, directly or indirectly, to people. This is because:

• Too much emphasis has been placed on measuring. While measurement is important, it represents 'siloed thinking'. In advancing the imperative to make the most of ecosystem services in cities, it is essential that we link UGI with outcomes for people's health and wellbeing, which will help to identify areas of immediate concern and guide our actions.

• There isn't enough understanding of the relationship between nature and people, especially around what matters to people and where it matters (known as *attribution*), and how much access to UGI is needed (known as *dosage*).

Based on this, we argue that Natural Capital (NC) can deliver UGI in cities because it can highlight potential solutions that would unlock the other four capitals: financial, human, social and manufactured.

1. Introduction

Let's start by framing the problem. Parallel and interconnected trends in global population, climate, resource availability and economic development pose significant challenges to the current western model for urban living. Indeed, the rapid growth in urban populations has led to inevitable concerns over the sustainability of city form and function, and the health of ecosystems and citizens.[1] Green and blue spaces in cities (hereafter termed Urban Green Infrastructure – UGI), the stuff that delivers ecological services (ES),[2] accounts for 14% of urban space in the UK[3] and between 1.9% and 46 % in other European cities.[4] This is highly variable, and worryingly, urbanisation has made, and is making, matters worse, leading to a net loss of this essential urban resource in some places.[5] So this made us think: in these challenging political times where money and staffing resources are limited, can we work towards a new model of governance that emphasises the key role for ecological services in cities and puts it at the core of city decision-making?

From the outset, our vision for the research was framed in social-ecological terms, in which we saw a city where air, sound and light pollution are minimised, and where transport routes, industrial activities and buildings are harmonised with green infrastructure to maximise social cohesion, the economy *and* human wellbeing. Such a city would make a chance encounter with 'the natural in the built' a daily, commonplace experience and make ecological service provision more equitable, irrespective of class, diversity, age or gender.[6]

---

[1]   Grimm et al. 2008. Global Change and the Ecology of Cities. *Science*, **319**(5864), 756–760.

[2]   See *Millennium Ecosystem Assessment*: https://www.millenniumassessment.org/en/Global. html

[3]   Davies et al. 2011. Urban. In: *The UK National Ecosystem Technical Report*. UNEP-WCMC, pp. 361-410. Cambridge.

[4]   Fuller & Gaston 2009. The scaling of green space coverage in European cities. *Biology Letters*, **5**(3), 352-355.

[5]   e.g. Dallimer et al. 2011. Temporal changes in greenspace in a highly urbanized region. *Biology Letters*, **7**(5), 763–766.

[6]   See Republica 2015. *A community right to beauty*: http://www.respublica.org.uk/wp-content/ uploads/2015/07/Right-to-Beauty-Final-1.pdf

The vision also highlights the important synergies and relationships between daily *journeys*, such as the school run and the daily commute, with *place*, including home, work, parks and retail outlets, and the multifunctional role that UGI may play in this dynamic.

We address this vision by using our work to characterise the elements of what an *ecosystem serviced city* is and understand how it functions. We did this by using a sequence of discussion points to address the work we've undertaken. We start by defining key terms and then commenting on previous ES studies where people were of central importance. We use a simple 'thought experiment' to outline the complex relationships of people with their environment and then centre the debate on health and wellbeing as a means of gaining traction on policy. This is followed by an analysis of how ES are integrated into city planning and policy systems. We end with some recommendations on how to deliver ES in cities.

While our research speaks to the up and coming literature on city greening,[7] our focus will be on *citizen access to ecosystem services*, and how cities are experienced through our senses. In doing so, this research theme connects directly with those concerned with city wellbeing, aspirations and mobilities.[8] We start our discussion by aping Tony Juniper's excellent book (2013) "What has nature ever done for us?"[9]

[7] See Green infrastructure partnership: https://www.tcpa.org.uk/pages/category/green-infrastructure-partnership

[8] See *The Little Book of Wellbeing* and *The Little Book of Mobilities in the City* in the Little Book series.

[9] Tony Juniper 2013. *What has nature ever done for us? How money really does grow on trees.* Profile Books, London.

2. Natural capital, ecosystem services and green infrastructure - in cities

To address this question, we first need to introduce the concepts of Urban Green Infrastructure (UGI), Ecological Services (ES) and Natural Capital (NC). These concepts have a long and rich history in the academic literature, dating back for decades – 1985 for UGI, 1990s for NC, and mid-1990s for ES.

UGI has been defined as *"an interconnected network of greenspace that conserves natural ecosystem values and functions and provides associated benefits to human populations*".[10] It captures a multifunctional and networked view of green habitats in cities, and because of this, has gained considerable traction in planning and landscape circles.

We adopt the Natural Capital Committee's definition of NC as: *"the world's stocks of natural assets which include geology, soil, air, water and all living things"*.[11] The links between UGI and NC are clearly visible; they both relate to the physical variability of natural habitats and species in landscapes. While NC focusses attention on the *stocks of resources*, UGI emphasises the *interrelationships between things in the landscape*.

Here, we use the broad definition of ES as the benefits *provided by natural ecosystems that contribute to making human life both possible and worth living*. The 2005 Millennium Ecosystem Assessment[12] suggests the following four categories for ES (Figure 1):

- *Provisioning Services*, which supply goods for people, including drinking water, crops and resources, like timber and fuel.

- *Regulating Services*, which maintain desirable qualities, such as buffering temperature extremes, water purification and storage.

- *Cultural Services*, which have direct social value, like health benefits and recreation opportunities.

- *Supporting Services*, which underpin the delivery of services, including primary production and nutrient cycling.

There is considerable confusion in the use of these terms – all are used interchangeably in the academic literature, especially ES and NC. For ES thinking to be adopted by a wider group of stakeholders, rather than the usual candidates, the language needs to be accessible to all, including policy makers, academics, businesses and the wider public. Only then can we design reporting frameworks based on measurement and monitoring. We'll explore this point elsewhere in this book.

---

[10] Benedict & McMahon 2002. Green infrastructure: Smart conservation for the 21st century. *Renewable Resources Journal*, **20**(3), 12–17.

[11] Natural Capital Committee Third Report 2015. www.gov.uk/government/publications/natural-capital-committees-third-state-of-natural-capital-report

[12] Millennium Ecosystem Assessment 2005. *Ecosystems and human well-being*. Island Press Washington, DC.

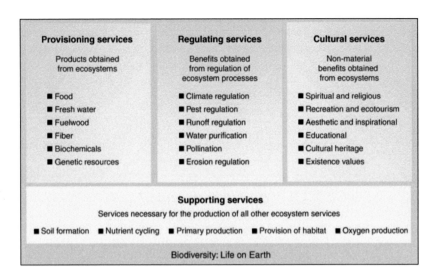

Figure 1. Ecological ecosystem services provided by natural environments (Source: MEA website)

The links between UGI, ES and NC can be viewed in terms of a *form-function-service provision framework* (Figure 2), where UGI captures the spatial structure and function of the green network in cities. Delivery of ES is related to the form-function links, while NC relates to the stock of natural assets. It is from NC that humans derive ES, which make human life possible. The benefits that people gain from ES then relate to the nature of their interactions with it (we develop this idea later). For example, the city has a physical form, which can be mapped, and UGI provides an ecological function, such as pollination. This function then provides a service – again pollination – which in this case supports food production. As each city has a different urban form, different outcomes in service provision can be expected. Sadly, some ecosystem services are being used by humanity so rapidly that the stocks of natural capital are being depleted at unsustainable rates. This is a specific issue in cities where NC stocks are low anyway, and is exacerbated where NC is currently, and often massively, under-valued.

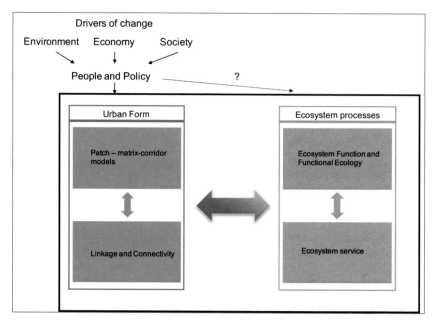

Figure 2. The links between urban form, ecological function and ecological services.

2.1 ES mapping in cities

As cities are varied mixes of grey (e.g. roads) and green (e.g. parks) infrastructure, arranged in a diverse manner, ES studies have focused on mapping the variability in UGI.

In applying ES thinking to urban areas, it is worth noting how the various forms of service might operate at a city scale (Figure 3). Cities are spatially bounded, resource intensive spaces that import and use more than can be generated locally.[13]

---

[13]   Herbert Girardet 2015. *Creating Regenerative Cities.* Routledge, Oxford.

A large body of work emphasises several means by which such services improve the urban environment to deliver ES[14] – such as climate amelioration,[15] carbon sequestration and storage,[16] floodwater storage and urban water,[17] and air purification[18] – and support rich assemblages of wildlife that have recreational and aesthetic value.[19]

Important though these analyses are, they only get us part of the way towards a solution and are characterised by quick-win outcomes. The explicit focus on mapping things - that is, NC and UGI - means we essentially remove people from the equation, which may lead to the potential commercialisation of nature implied by the language of *infrastructure, capital* and *services*. This poses a more practical risk: its diverse functions will become simplified through easily measureable metrics, but it will not necessarily measure those that are harder to capture, such as Cultural Urban Ecological Services (CUES). The work thus fails to develop a framework that places people at the centre of the debate, nor does it evaluate the complex rhythm of city life over time and space. We argue that delivery of ES with people in mind needs to be the focus of planning and visioning activities. We explain why in the next section.

---

[14] Haase et al. 2014. A Quantitative Review of Urban Ecosystem Service Assessments: Concepts, Models, and Implementation. *AMBIO*, **43**(4), 413–433.

[15] Akbari et al. 2001. Cool surfaces and shade trees to reduce energy use and improve air quality in urban areas. *Solar Energy*, **70**(3), 295–310.

[16] Nowak & Crane 2002. Carbon storage and sequestration by urban trees in the USA. *Environ. Pollution*, **116**(3), 381–9.

[17] Eigenbrod et al. 2011. The impact of projected increases in urbanization on ecosystem services. *Proc. Roy. Soc. Lon. B*, **278**(1722), 3201–3208.

[18] Pugh et al. 2012. Effectiveness of Green Infrastructure for Improvement of Air Quality in Urban Street Canyons. *Environ. Sci. Tech.*, **46**, 7692-7699.

[19] Dearborn & Kark 2010. Motivations for Conserving Urban Biodiversity. *Conservation Biology*, **24**, 432–440.

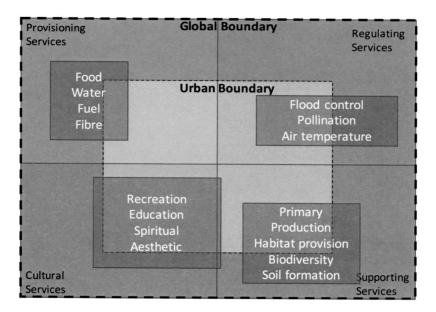

Figure 3. Ecosystem services consumed by urban citizens (blue boxes). Provisioning services mostly produced outside the city. Cultural and regulating services are often produced and consumed within city boundaries.

3. Natural capital, ecosystem services and green infrastructure - for people

Our starting point here originates from a chance reading of a book by Paul Rodaway,[20] published in 1994. In this book, Rodaway explored how humans interact with nature and natural landscapes through our senses; we'll call these Sensescapes.

---

[20] Paul Rodaway 1994. *Sensuous Geographies: Body, Sense and Place.* Routledge, London and New York.

Because we all experience cities in different ways, we have a range of emotional responses to what's around us (we develop this theme more below).

3.1 Thinking the issue through

We wanted to show the complexity of the issues discussed above by conducting a small thought experiment that highlights the need to focus ES on the delivery of CUES and to explore nature and natural landscapes through our senses (Box 1).

Box 1: A day in the life of Janet

Janet lives in a large city. This city is heavily designed around the use of the car, with city centre businesses dominating the economy. It is characterised by poor and ageing transport systems, but there is some development of infrastructure for alternative modes of transport (e.g., cycling and walking). Problems related to summertime heat and air and noise pollution are both significant and pressing. Moreover, like many global cities, it is a 24-hour operation, lit as brightly at night as it is in the day.

Janet starts her day, like many parents, with the school run. She can either use the car to make a 5-minute trip to school (in good traffic conditions) or take the walking bus and accompany her child from pick up point to the school (a round trip of 30-40 minutes). If the traffic is heavy, she can sit in the car for an additional 30 minutes in an environment where exhaust fumes are concentrated into her car. If she walks to school avoiding the main routes, she can avoid traffic pollution and experience natural sound, enjoy the walk and the views with possible encounters with wildlife en route. She can also get rained on, cold from biting winds and encounter the odd angry and aggressive dog in the local park.

After dropping off her child at school, she can either take the car into work – a 45-minute journey in rush hour – navigating one the two main arterial routes into the city, or she can opt to drive to the local park-and-ride terminus and chance the local train, which is frequently subject to delays and excessive over-crowding. At least she'll avoid the pollution until she arrives in the central station, which is mainly below ground and heavily polluted with diesel fumes from the ageing, rolling stock. The walk from the central station to her place of work is 10 minutes along traffic-filled roads. Her workplace is in a refurbished factory with multiple units crammed into the space, several of them with very little in the way of external views or natural light. The office is a 20-minute walk from the nearest greenspace.

She leaves work at 15.30 to collect her child from school, either in the car or on foot. At home, she has access to a large back garden in her 1930s, semi-detached property. It's her pride and joy, planted carefully with shrubs and trees to attract wildlife. It's an outdoor room for the family, especially during summer, but even in winter, it provides respite through the view.

Looking at the fictional excerpt from Janet's day, what's interesting is that the places remain relatively constant. The office environment doesn't change much, but her home can be modified to accommodate additional UGI elements. Moreover, the view of the garden changes over the day and night, with changing light and weather conditions, and also seasonally. However, she has choices in how she moves between the places where she works and lives. She can choose to walk and use public transport, and engage more fully with the natural environment or drive to work and view the environment through a car windscreen. The links between how she chooses to commute and her variable interaction with ES provision are clear to see. This determines, if you wish, her daily dose of 'green wellbeing'. It will be different depending on the choices she makes. For example, if she chooses to take up cycling as a commute, she can ride down the recently resurfaced and improved canal towpath and interact with ES in other ways. Whatever she does, she can still recharge at home in the garden, even if she's had an awful day in the office. A growing body of literature indicates that human-environment interaction, as people go about their daily lives, has an influential and important role to play in their wellbeing.

3.2 Green - health links

We sharpen the focus in this section by emphasising the role of CUES in delivering enhanced health and wellbeing outcomes for people living in cities. We argue that this explicit focus on health and health outcomes has two key benefits. First, it helps to research ES at an appropriate scale; for example, from the individual to the city and from day into night. Secondly, if flipped and viewed as savings in healthcare provision, it has the potential to unlock resources that have been siloed and misaligned in the past.

A substantial and influential body of academic evidence emphasises the important role of UGI provision in cities in enhancing human health.[21] The evidence base showing the importance of green health benefits can be grouped into three types:

- Epidemiological studies linking health benefits of exposure to CUES to an improved natural environment.

- Epidemiological evidence linking green space to behavioural changes leading to increased levels of physical exercise.

- Improvements in psychological (mental) health engendered by exposure to natural places and scenes.

Epidemiological studies include a wide range of self-reported, epidemiological health studies[22] and morbidity and mortality studies.[23] Several of these emphasise how UGI is linked to behavioural and physiological changes; for example, in relation to self-reported physical activity,[24] BMI and enhanced psychological outcomes for people living in areas adjacent to green environments in cities.[25]

Several researchers have argued that the distinctions between people, ecological services – expressed through place – and health are contrived, and that there is a need to reconceptualise or reimagine the relationship between the variables to emphasise their complexity, history and how they manifest themselves in health outcomes and individual behaviours.[26] This sentiment is shared by a growing number of health professionals[27] who suggest that more emphasis needs to be placed on researching what kinds of ecological services are consumed.

---

[21] Tzoulas et al. 2007. Promoting ecosystem and human health in urban areas using Green Infrastructure: A literature review. *Landscape and Urban Planning*, **81**(3), 167–178.

[22] Maas et al. 2006. Green space, urbanity, and health: how strong is the relation? *J. Epidemiol. Comm. Health*, **60**(7), 587–592.

[23] Mitchell & Popham 2007. Greenspace, urbanity and health: relationships in England. *J. Epidemiol. Comm. Health*, **61**(8), 681–683.

[24] Li et al. 2005. Multilevel modelling of built environment characteristics related to neighbourhood walking activity in older adults. *J. Epidemiol. Comm. Health*, **59**(7), 558-564.

[25] Reviewed in Sadler et al. 2010. Getting life into cities: the importance of greenspace for people and biodiversity. In Gaston (ed.) *Urban Ecology*. Cambridge University Press.

[26] Tunstall et al. 2004. Places and health. *J. Epidemiol. Comm. Health*, **58**(1), 6-10.

[27] Frumkin 2003. Healthy places: Exploring the evidence. *Am. J. Pub. Health*, **93**, 1451-1456.

In addition, which, and where, people receive ecological services is a question of considerable importance, as the academic literature clearly indicates strong health inequalities in most cities in relation to proximity and access to nature.[28]

What is being viewed or 'experienced' is a more difficult problem. We know of work that captures the relationship between peoples' self-reported wellbeing, measured physiological outcomes, like reduced blood pressure, and elements of biodiversity, such as habitat structure,[29] charismatic wildlife species,[30] bird song,[31] other natural sound[32] and so on. However, there is little work that clearly focuses on our individual responses to ES, including how much exposure to ES is needed to feel good; this is important and requires further research. What we do know, though, is that there is sufficient evidence for putting the wellbeing of citizens in the centre of the *ecosystem serviced city* idea.

3.3 Linking people to the delivery of ES

ES mapping becomes more meaningful when combined with other sources of information that relate directly to people.[33] We illustrate this with two examples using Birmingham as a case study.

---

[28]   Heynen 2006. Green urban political ecologies: toward a better understanding of inner city environmental change. *Environ. Planning A*, **38**(3), 499-516.

[29]   Shanahan et al. 2016. Health Benefits from Nature Experiences Depend on Dose. *Sci. Rep.*, **6**, 28551.

[30]   Cox et al. 2017. Doses of Neighborhood Nature: The Benefits for Mental Health of Living with Nature. *Bioscience*, **67**(2), 147-155.

[31]   Hedblom et al. 2014. Bird song diversity influences young people's appreciation of urban landscapes. *Urb. For. Urban Green.*, **13**(3), 469-474.

[32]   Aiello et al. 2016. Chatty maps: constructing sound maps of urban areas from social media data. *Royal. Soc. Open Sci.*, **3**, 150690.

[33]   More examples can be found in Church et al. 2014. UK National Ecosystem Assessment Follow-on. Work Package Report 5: Cultural ecosystem services and indicators. UNEP-WCMC, LWEC, UK.

3.3.1 Built surface cover and its response to elevated temperatures

Built surface cover in cities generally has a low albedo, which refers to its reflective qualities, and a high capacity to store and radiate heat. In contrast, vegetated surfaces typically reflect more solar radiation, store and radiate less heat, and also actively cool surfaces during the day through evapotranspiration. To confirm these differences between built and vegetated surface cover, we analysed how urban vegetation cover helped to reduce air temperature extremes during a heat wave in Birmingham at 22.00 hours on 23rd July 2013. The analysis used a regression-based, land-use approach, similar to the urban climate zones advocated by some climatologists.[34] It linked heat stress outcomes to data from the UK 2011 Census Ecosystem and showed differences between age groups and households on various dimensions of deprivation, including unemployment, low levels of education, bad health and poor accommodation.

Figure 4 shows the differences in temperature during the episode and indicates substantial spatial variability. When linked with the demographic and deprivation data, we found that only 24% of 0-4 year old children in Birmingham lived in areas that are 2.5°C cooler than the maximum recorded during the event, whilst 95% of children live in areas that are at least 1°C cooler (Table 1). Moreover, those suffering from all four dimensions of deprivation were much less likely to live in areas that are relatively cool during a heat wave when compared with those who suffer from no deprivation.

3.3.2 Conformity with green space standards

The second example concerns Natural England's Accessible Natural Greenspace Standards[35] (ANGSt) that were created to provide nationwide standards for guidance on residents' access to urban greenspaces. To conform to the ANGSt standard, we chose locations that were no more than 300m away from public open spaces, greater than 2 hectares in size and which were dominated by vegetation or open water. The results from this analysis indicate that half of the city population has poor access to

---

[34] Stewart & Oke. 2012. Local climate zones for urban climatology. *BAMS*, DOI:10.1175/BAMS-D-11-00019.1. Note we are aware of the issues in these correlative approaches but the point is it allows planners to consider likely societal impacts, while spatializing the outcomes.

[35] Natural England's ANGSt standards: www.naturalengland.org.uk/regions/east_of_england/ourwork/gi/accessiblenaturalgreenspacestandardangst

Figure 4. A linear model predicting air temperature at 22.00 hours during a heat wave in Birmingham, based on the percentage vegetated surface cover within 100m of the measurement locations. Temperatures range from 18.0°C (blue) to 22.5°C (red).

public greenspace (Figure 5). This is surprising, as Birmingham has an abundance of green spaces, but many of them are smaller than the 2-hectare threshold applied.

Together, these analyses demonstrate that it is possible to estimate the performance of ES at a high social as well as physical spatial resolution. We also saw that each service performed poorly in the city centre, but few other similarities existed (see Table 1). The equity issues identified using the air temperature metric provide an interesting overview at the city level, but may well mask variations at a local scale. For example, an analysis of a different heat wave from the one in the first example found that those living in the city centre – where the temperature extremes are greatest – were divided into two groups at opposite ends of the socio-economic spectrum, and with strongly contrasting levels of heat risk. Similarly, access to greenspaces was different, depending on where you lived and how far you were from those greenspaces. These

Figure 5. Areas within 300m (light blue) of accessible greenspaces >2ha in area (purple) in Birmingham.

important links between environment and health were discussed in the Marmot Review.[36]

Mapping certainly provides a clearer vision of where issues may lie in relation to measureable outcomes, such as access, quality and inequality.[37] But are our city governance and planning systems up to the task of delivering improved outcomes?

[36] The Marmot Review 2010. Fair Society – Healthy Lives. www.local.gov.uk/marmot-review-report-fair-society-healthy-lives

[37] This is very well illustrated by Birmingham's Green Living Spaces Plan: www.birmingham.gov.uk/greenlivingspaces

Census reporting group	% population living in locations at least 2°C below the UHI maximum	% population with access to a greenspace > 2ha within 300m
Total city population	60	50
0-4year old children	56	54
75+ year olds	69	52
Adults not subject to any dimensions of deprivation	66	50
1 deprivation dimension	60	50
2 dimensions of deprivation	60	54
3 dimensions of deprivation	57	56
4 dimensions of deprivation	56	55

Table 1. Baseline performance parameters for selected ecosystem service

4. The need to re-evaluate the governance of municipal planning and finance for natural capital

To help us address this thorny question, we asked ourselves what local people, who benefit from NC in cities, and the ES that derive from it, thought about the UGI in their places. We have developed a strong argument (above) as to why ES delivery should be framed at the level of the individual without presenting evidence as to whether citizens want or desire this, or whether city systems are actually up to the task of delivering it. Our intention was to provide city decision-makers and city leaders with a clearer reason to use the economic, cultural, physical, political and social capitals at their disposal to encourage greater access to, and use of, UGI in the city. To assist in identifying key themes that highlight the tensions with, and barriers to, ES provision in cities, we also analysed interviews of actors working with UGI in cities (see Section 4.2).

4.1 *Highbury Parks Summit: a case study in localised visioning*

In 2016, Birmingham City Council received a public petition with 3,000 signatures calling for a greener city centre and the inclusion of a new public park at the heart of the planned redevelopment of an area of the city where the outdoor and indoor markets are currently situated. This coincided with the UK Government confirming in Autumn 2016 that it was committed to progressing a 25-year Environment Plan Framework document in response to their earlier Natural Environment White Paper (2011), stating that the Government would be the first ever *"... to return the environment in a better condition than it inherited it, over the course of a generation"*.

Also in the Autumn of 2016, the UK Government launched a Parliamentary Select Committee to review the Future of Public Parks with a specific brief to seek answers to four questions:

- Who uses Parks and why?
- What are the health benefits of Parks?
- What is the right administrative status for Parks?
- What are the future funding and management models for Parks?

Parallel, local political developments saw all London mayoral candidates back a public campaign to make London the first National Park City in the Spring of 2016, while in the Spring of 2017, the first mayoral elections took place in the West Midlands for a newly formed Combined Authority. Mimicking London's ambitions, the Birmingham Green Coalition called upon all candidates to support the development of a 25-year Environment (Natural Capital) Plan for Birmingham and the wider West Midlands that would follow the Government's final published framework.

It was in light of all these developments that Birmingham City Council approached the Liveable Cities team to facilitate the Birmingham Highbury Parks Summit.

4.1.1 Summit Outline

The event took place on November 2nd 2016 at Highbury Hall, Birmingham, facilitated by researchers from the Lancaster University. The morning event saw an invited audience drawn from the City's Well Being Panel: 30 were invited, 25 attended. The afternoon Workshop[38] saw 12 representatives of the main City Council Departments responsible for aspects of the City's environment, together with representation from the City's main partner and stakeholder organisations invited, with 27 attendees in total; 12 city council; 15 external partners.

The morning session used a *Future Visions Workshop Methodology*, allowing for free association to develop a range of headline items concerning UGI in the city. In this way, the Headline Items (Box 2) emerged with many underlying themes and connections, thereby emphasising the strength of feeling people had to certain issues and priorities. Unlocking these connections was one of the key outcomes of the afternoon session, which also examined the practicalities involved in implementing these ideas.

The afternoon workshop explored how these Headline Items could be implemented across Birmingham (Figure 7). This was done by assembling the items into 'boxes of thoughts' that could be shaped, linked and reframed by the participants. The outcome of this process was synthesised and reframed into four, higher-level themes (Table 2) that emphasised the connectivity between people, nature and their environment, civic pride in their 'UGI estate' and the need to revive, and in some cases, 're-find' core UGI assets. These four themes were linked more directly and formally to the delivery of enhanced wellbeing.

---

[38] 12 representatives across all relevant city council departments, health, sport, parks, planning, transport, etc.; 15 external partners, 4 local green charities, 2 community charities, 1 Wildlife Trust, 2 regional business groups, 2 regional sports bodies, 2 health and mental health groups, 1 Arts organization, 1 university.

Box 2: Highbury Parks Summit – Headline Items generated by members of the public

1. *Change the Way we Plan*

2. *Community Connectivity & Health*

3. *Greening the Grey*

4. *Learning to Take Pride in Birmingham*

5. *Revival*

6. *Activities for Wellbeing for Everyone*

7. *Come & Discover 'Undiscovered' Birmingham*

8. *Community Participation & Ownership*

9. *Keep Public Spaces Well Maintained*

10. *Maintaining & Developing Security and Safety*

11. *My Space My Responsibility*

12. *Pathways to Parks*

13. *Policy, Management & Supervision*

14. *Towards Greener Travel*

15. *Use it or Lose it*

Figure 6. Example of linking and connecting 'community connectivity and health'

Table 2: High-Level Highbury Parks Summit themes	
Get Nature to People and People to Nature (Headline Items: 10,12,15)	**Revive and Restore undiscovered Birmingham** (Headline Items: 5,7,9,13)
• A citywide communications strategy, *'Pathways to Parks'*, promoting the benefits of parks and nature, where to find it, what to look for and how to get there. • Link local sites with active travel routes and networks. • Prioritise engaging children and vulnerable people.	• Establish and publish environmental audit standards and new metrics for all parks and neighbourhoods. • Prioritise the restoration and revival of neglected parkland and rundown local areas. • Build local resilience. • Collaborative community projects to rediscover 'undiscovered' Birmingham.
Take Pride in a Greener Birmingham – Change the Way we Plan and Fund Green (Headline Items: 1,3,4,14)	**Create Wellbeing Communities with Parks at their Heart** (Headline Items: 2,6,8,11)
• Green the existing grey environments. • Mandate green in all developments. • Green City Partnership & levies. • Link up the citywide green & blue network. • Expand green travel options.	• Outdoor activity programmes for all. • Promote community participation and enable community governance, ownership and innovative economic activity. • Strengthen healthy living & productive landscapes.

4.1.2 Summit Outcome

We assembled the four themes from the Highbury Parks Summit and aligned them with the four questions we asked on Liveable Cities, the four pillars of the first draft 25-year Environment Plan Framework, the eight economic priorities identified by the West Midlands Combined Authority and Birmingham City Council's strategic priorities (Children, Housing, Health and Jobs and Skills), (Table 3). Based on this, we generated three key recommendations:

1. Create a Vision Statement outlining the key commitments to be delivered through a 25-year environment plan and create an associated communications plan to sit alongside this.

2. Agree on a set of delivery principles for implementation of a 25-year plan that aims to increase NC stocks in cities by all key stakeholders.

3. Create an executive summary document that captures all of the above and use this to seek widespread public and political support, including the West Midlands Combined Authority mayoral candidates.

Table 3: Alignment of peoples' visions to strategic planning initiatives				
Existing Frameworks	Strategic Priority 1	Strategic Priority 2	Strategic Priority 3	Strategic Priority 4
Highbury Parks Summit's 4 Outcomes	Get Nature to People and People to Nature	Revive and Restore Undiscovered Birmingham	Take Pride in a Greener Birmingham – Change the Way we Plan & Fund Green	Create Wellbeing Communities with Parks at their Heart
Liveable Cities' four Questions	Who benefits from ES and how?	What are the multiple values for ES and what are the metrics?	What are the sustainable funding mechanisms for ES?	What are the appropriate governance model(s) for ES?
25-Year four pillars	Connecting Nature with People	Environmental Decision-Making & Data	Effective Regulatory and Funding Models	Environmental Delivery Mechanisms
West Midlands Combined Authority's 8 priorities	Medical & Life Sciences	Creative & Digital	New Manufacturing Economy	HS2 Growth
	Environmental Technologies	Housing	Skills for Employment & Growth	Exploiting Economic Geography
Birmingham City Council's 4 strategic priorities	Children	Housing	Jobs and Skills	Health

4.2 Practitioner - user - activist perspectives

Here, we consider the perspective of the practitioners, activists and users who play significant roles in relation to the green spaces, natural life and sustainability agendas in three case study cities: Birmingham, Amsterdam and Belfast. All of our 27 interviewees were identified and selected for their knowledge and involvement in these areas and offer a broad and representative sample of civil servants, volunteers, charity workers, environmental and urban activists, and environment and urban design professionals. The interviews were carried out by Dr Martin Locret-Collet as part of his doctoral study.[39] From the many hours of transcribed material, it is possible to identify themes common to all cities in terms of how UGI is managed, used and experienced. We focus here on the commonalities, not the important differences, that one might expect in cities with very different cultural and social histories. Nor do we elaborate on how these spaces are reconfigured, appropriated and can be theorised using different perspectives. Below are three example quotes from just 3 interviewees, one from each city.

First, the importance and need for protection of the UGI was universally emphasised by all, although there was a diversity of visions on how this might be achieved:

- Even though the multi-functionality of green spaces and the importance of ES in delivering multiple benefits in terms of reducing temperatures and alleviating flood risks, for example, were widely acknowledged, several practitioners promoted better health as a key driver at a political and policy level.

> *"Access to public open space ... good quality public open space, it is important, not just any public open space but good quality open space, there's massive links to health benefits"* (Head of Parks, Birmingham City Council, 12/01/15).

Secondly, while recognising the need for UGI protection, or at the very least, the requirement for more sensitive management, the lack of long-term visioning and planning emerged as an issue requiring some thought, notwithstanding the proliferation of grand schemes and masterplans:

---

[39] Martin Locret-Collet 2016. *Commoning our futures? An anarchist urban political ecology.* PhD thesis, University of Birmingham.

- Third, lack of continuity in policies and environmental programmes highlights the complex, temporal situation, where short-sightedness and a lack of coordination of decision-makers, due in part to a rapid turnover in political structures, has stymied cities from managing UGI in a manner in tune with longer timescales on which natural landscapes operate – these timescales are inter-generational.

"At the same time, I'm a little bit critical, that's, I guess, typical from politics as well that there's a lot of things happening that are already forming a foundation, and they are overlooked very often and they may even disappear. [...] Of course, every four years you have the new election and it can change the way you work. [...] Yeah, every four years everything is insecure" (Programme Manager for Nature and Environmental Education, Municipality of Amsterdam, 21/10/14)

The urgent need for new ways of thinking about UGI sustainability, characterised by a broader understanding of values, was also prevalent in the responses, especially in terms of the key role that UGI plays as 'social cement', helping to bind communities to place.

"And we've had... we've seen kids that had visited, we've had open days where we've had kids from all over, all over East Belfast attending... So the idea is that this is sort of a neutral area where people can come together and hopefully enjoy the space. I'm hoping in the next year too that, like I said the surrounding areas will benefit from this little green piece of land. Yeah" (Project Manager, Bridge Community Garden, Belfast,13/03/15).

Taken as a whole, this narrative shines a light on the heart of the problem: disjunctions and misalignment in planning, governance and finance frameworks surrounding UGI.

4.2 The Heart of the problem - A Planning-Governance-Finance UGI conundrum

A planning-governance-finance conundrum has existed in the UK for at least the last 100 years, but the situation has now become acute. The UK planning system is caught in a dilemma: the National Planning Policy Framework,[40] the formative document for the planning profession and developers, states that biodiversity should incur 'no net loss', yet the UK Government also wrote the Natural Environment White Paper, which includes a commitment to NC and a generational ambition for improvement in its status. The difference in language and concepts used within these and other policy documents means that UGI remains obscure and overly complex.[41] In addition, the people involved in writing, reading and contributing to these documents will have wildly different views on how UGI should be planned for and managed.

Multiple and frequently conflicting demands, such as housing, manufacturing, energy, health and natural conservation objectives, are often pursued in their own siloes. This has recently been exemplified by the Parliamentary Enquiry into '*The Future of Parks*',[42] which exposed how the future of UGI requires rethinking, not only within planning,[43] but also in governance and finance. This divide has deeper roots, causing a physical and mental disconnection between people and UGI in cities. This, in turn, is reflected in how UGI is thought about in political and organisational structures, how it is financed and how it is connected (or not) as a network to the people it serves.

[40] NPPF: www.gov.uk/guidance/national-planning-policy-framework

[41] Scott et al. 2014. Tools – Applications, Benefits and Linkages for Ecosystem Science (TABLES), Final Report to the UNEPWMC Research Councils UK, Welsh Government and Defra, June, UNEP-WCMC, LWEC, UK.

[42] Future of Parks Report: www.parliament.uk/business/committees/committees-a-z/ commons-select/communities-and-local-government-committee/inquiries/parliament-2015/ public-parks-16-17

[43] Scott AJ et al. (2013) Disintegrated Development at the Rural Urban Fringe: Re-connecting spatial planning theory and practice. *Progress in Planning*, **83**, 1-52.

5. Re-envisioning delivery of Ecosystem Services in cities

5.1 A new delivery framework

In order to tackle the integration of municipal planning, finance and governance – a point also emphasised by the UN in their New Urban Agenda[44] – we undertook a systems thinking exercise that traced the connections between all those operations or activities in a city that involve UGI in some way (Figure 8). What emerged was a map of the possible beneficiaries of UGI; however, we managed to reveal more than the usual suspects, like dog walkers and the local football team who use local greenspaces. Suddenly, the NHS and big business appear as connected beneficiaries,

---

[44] United Nations – New Urban Agenda 2016: habitat3.org/the-new-urban-agenda

rather than as direct beneficiaries. Between all these connections, you can see both strong and weak ties, and, equally important, connections between those individual beneficiaries. What emerged were several groupings, which, when analysed, were seen to fit six broad headings that we termed Communities of Practice and which form the basis of the Star Framework (see Figure 9).

When we stand back from the Star Framework and review what it is that these Communities of Practice represent, several things come to light. First, they represent what Forum for the Future describes as the five capitals: financial, human, manufactured, social and natural capital.[45] By bringing NC into the complex matter of city decision-making, there can be some truly integrated solutions. For Birmingham, the second thing that emerged was the clear identification of the four strategic priorities: Housing, Health, Children and Jobs and Skills. The final important part of this framework is the position of governance itself: it is effectively the keystone upon which the success or failure of decisions stand.

The idea behind this framework is to design a joined-up, co-created set of metrics for each of the six Communities of Practice that can be used in business cases for change, business models to enable that change to happen and assurance frameworks to make visible the benefits of investment in ES and potentially attract new investment. Even more importantly, we would like to see ownership of this issue taken on from this point forward. This helps put NC at the heart of city decision-making and the metrics at the heart of the city's growth agenda. For this to happen, there is a clear need to bring Communities of Practice to the table to:

1. Take stock and evaluate the current situation.

2. Explain the new value-capture agenda and then agree on a common set of UGI indices.

3. Test and evaluate these in the field.

4. Use that process as a way to help solve the planning-governance-finance conundrum by specifically focussing on future models of procurement that capture wider values for UGI.

---

[45] Forum for the Future: www.forumforthefuture.org

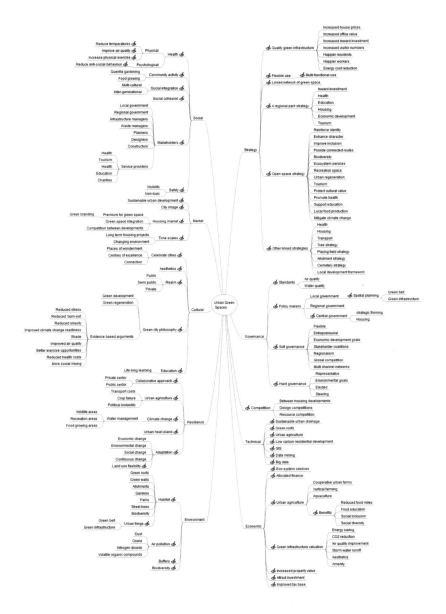

Figure 7. A system map focussing on urban green spaces

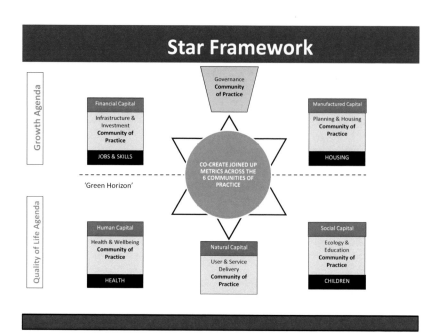

Figure 8. The STAR framework

The final thing to say about the Star Framework is how the three topics below the horizontal axis effectively represent what are commonly referred to as '*quality of life*' matters, whereas the three above the line are commonly looked upon as central to the '*growth agenda*'. However, this is where 'growth' is too narrowly defined, particularly in times of austerity. The horizontal axis in this diagram is labelled the '*green horizon*' as it represents an effective glass ceiling - whereby these matters do not get full recognition in major city decision-making processes. So the multiple benefits of nature in cities discussed in this book are obscured from the view of the decision makers. This again highlights the need for cities to more closely link the municipal functions of planning, finance and governance.

35

5.2 An engagement and reporting framework

On a global scale, there are a few significant programmes underway involving direct, Natural Capital investment. These tend to fall into two camps: big businesses, who invest to reduce their production risks, or nation states implementing schemes at a national scale. However, these remain the exception, rather than the rule, so what all parties are seeking is to make these practices mainstream through a bringing together of approaches and methodologies. To help this process, the Natural Capital Coalition has published its Protocol and a series of Sector Guides.[46]

The challenge we have set ourselves for Birmingham and the wider West Midlands Combined Authority is: could this approach be applied to a city-region? Could the benefits from NC co-investment be made visible to the key stakeholders across the local economic community? The benefits of NC are currently captured through a combination of performance and assurance frameworks, both of which are monitored through a joint economic tool. Our recommendation is to build a NC module across that monitoring tool, the content of which is co-designed with key stakeholders so that we reach a point where each of the 8 economic pillars of the strategic economic plan (see Table 3) have their own NC value-capture mechanism.

In turn, the NC module for the city-region could be developed as a sector guide, or cities protocol, for further global testing. It is essential that this point is reached if we are to achieve the necessary step change in our acknowledgement of our dependency on NC. Once this dependency is recognised, what follows is a re-balancing of how we value and re-invest in NC right across the economy so that responsibility for environmental restoration is not confined to the margins of special interest groups, but becomes a centrally understood and accepted way forward.

[46] www.naturalcapitalcoalition.org/protocol/sector-guides

6. Summary

The Liveable Cities project vision was to transform the engineering of cities to deliver global and societal wellbeing within the context of low carbon living and resource security through developing realistic and radical engineering that demonstrated the concept of an alternative future.

In this Little Book, we have presented a re-imagining of nature in cities and a radical rethink of how cities could see the future of their public parks and natural environment. It shows how nature could sit at the centre of decision-making when considering how better to more closely combine the municipal functions of planning, finance and governance. This process and rethink must extend beyond the bureaucratic boundaries of city administrations to embrace all citizens and the hidden wider beneficiaries or key future stakeholders - represented here by Communities of Practice.

All the evidence and arguments presented herein rotate around redefining value. This is one of the central challenges cities face in the 21st century and represents a key finding from the overall Liveable Cities project. In order to respond positively to the global pressures brought about by over half the world's population choosing to live in cities, new mechanisms need to be urgently introduced based on a whole systems approach where natural and built ecosystems are viewed as one city system. For the reasons emphasised in this publication, this must include nature and fully recognise the ES it provides, both to individuals and to the wider functions of any city.

If viewed in this way, the presence of nature in cities becomes something of real importance, sitting, we would argue, higher up the agenda than is currently the case. A business case can be made as to why the wider beneficiaries need to include nature in their balance sheets. The growth agenda for any city needs to include targets for re-building the presence of nature in cities and critically improving people's connections with it. It is clear from the people's views captured through this work just how highly they regard nature in cities. Following the advances represented in this Little Book, what is needed now is an urgent stock-take and pause in cities worldwide to question how the evidence contained here might influence their thinking going forward. How can a new future be built for cities that puts nature at the heart of decision-making and what might the benefits of doing so really look like?

Resources

This is a small section containing websites about ecosystem services, green city networks, several influential guidance reports, digital data and further reading. Doubtless there are more, many of these may be are pertinent to our narrative, but these are the websites and sources of reading material we enjoyed.

The Biophilic Cities Network:

http://biophiliccities.org

Foresight report on the future of the urban environment and ecosystem services in the UK:

https://www.gov.uk/government/uploads/system/uploads/attachment_data/file/469798/gs-15-34-future-cities-ecosystems.pdf

Millennium Ecosystem Assessment:

https://www.millenniumassessment.org/en/index.html

Nature of Cities Website:

https://www.thenatureofcities.com

Ordnance Survey Greenspace map:

https://www.ordnancesurvey.co.uk/getoutside/greenspaces/

Parliamentary Office of Science and Technology notes (POST-PN-0538 – Greenspace and Health):

http://researchbriefings.parliament.uk/ResearchBriefing/Summary/POST-PN-0538

Parliamentary Office of Science and Technology notes (POST-PN-448 – Urban Green Infrastructure):

http://researchbriefings.parliament.uk/ResearchBriefing/Summary/POST-PN-448#fullreport

United Nations – New Urban Agenda:

http://habitat3.org/the-new-urban-agenda/